The BROONS

D.C. THOMSON & Co. Ltd., GLASGOW: LONDON: DUNDEE

THE Broons

IN Spring, oot come the dusters—
   That fills Paw with dismay.
While Maw and the lassies sweep and shine,
Paw Broon gets clean—away!

In Summer, Daph and Maggie seek
A tan as the sun beats doon.
What matter if it comes on rain?
They'll still end up a' Broon!

In Autumn, while smart Horace swots,
It's " conker " time for others.
And then oor brainy lad is driven
" Nutty " by his brothers!

In Winter, when the snow lies thick,
Some creatures hibernate.
But no' oor lot! In fact, you'll see
The Broons in duplicate!

Well, that's the Broons. But if you want
Tae see them ALL year round,
Then order up " The Sunday Post "—
For that's where they are found!

Printed and published by D. C. Thomson & Co., Ltd., 185 Fleet Street, London, EC4A 2HS.
© D. C. Thomson & Co., Ltd., 1981
ISBN 0 85116 224 X

See Paw's face drop—

When the toaster goes " Pop "!

Stand by for a big ho-ho—

With the Bairn's eskimo!

Yak-yak-yak! Waffle! Blether!—
Nae wonder Paw's at the end o' his tether!

Jeannie wi' the shining hair—

Fills poor Hen Broon wi' despair!

You'll laugh, no' half—

At THIS photograph!

Behind a' this reek—

Is the fresh air they seek!

Whit a shock for Daphne when—

Her new lad's on the telly again!

Paw Broon's going to get big shocks—

When he shoves his hand through the letter-box!

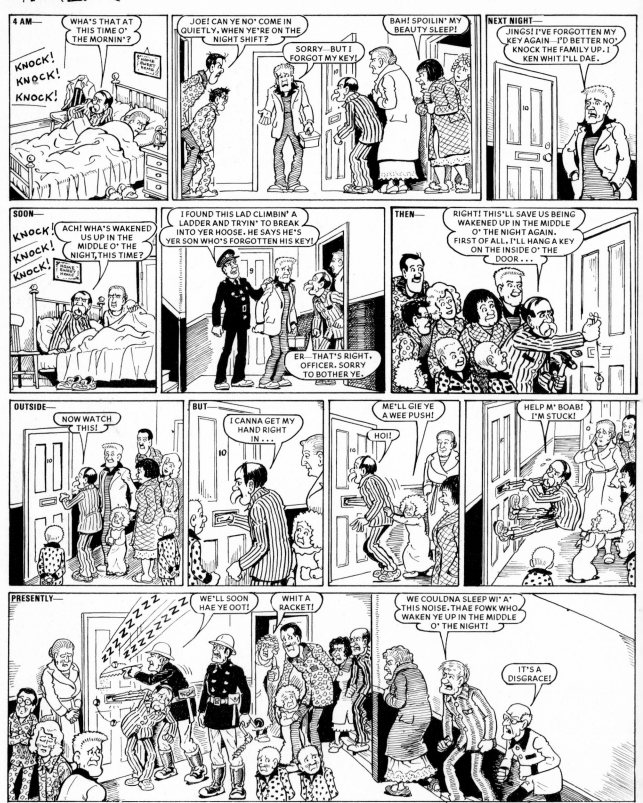

Help m'boab! It's no' half funny—

When Daphne turns into a bunny!

The tale o' the reckless cyclist who—

Got more than a hundred lines to do!

Why does Gran'paw need a comb—

When he's got a baldie dome?

This story's a' aboot—

Folks wi' names that suit.

Whit a come-doon for poor Paw—

He gets a carry-oot after a'!

The Bairn's a glutton—

For this kind o' Butt'ns

Betsy, Daisy and Lizzie—

Land Maggie in a tizzy!

There isna any doot—

He's a smashin' substitute!

Rule Number One—

Get your own job done!

When you've soup tae sup—

Keep your moustache up!

... but who made that—

Shadow of a cat?

The decision Maw's made—

Puts Paw in the " shade "!

Whit's the auld yin up to now?—

He's got them worried stiff, and how!

He's a dab hand wi' a brush—

But what's a' the rush?

Here's a laugh! Stand by for—

The great Glensporran tug-o'-war!

AT THE BUT-AN'-BEN. WE'RE AFF TO THE GLEN SPORRAN GAMES. WE'RE IN THE TUG O' WAR.

WAIT FOR ME! I'M COMIN' TOO. I LOVE WATCHIN' THOSE BIG STRONG MEN.

YOU CAN'T GO WEARIN' THOSE! THE FIELD'S AWFY MUDDY. YOU'LL RUIN YOUR SHOES.

I SUPPOSE YOU'RE RIGHT.

SO— GOOD, NOBODY'S SEEN ME.

OH! AREN'T THEY LOVELY?

LATER— IT'S NEARLY FINISHED. I'LL SNEAK OFF BEFORE THEY GET A GOOD LOOK AT ME.

WHIT HAPPENED TO YOUR SISTER, LADS? SHE LEFT BEFORE THE END.

I DINNA KEN, SANDY.

ER—COULD YOU COME IN FOR A MINUTE, LADS?

HO-HO! DAPHNE'S WELLIES ARE STUCK!

WE'LL SOON HAVE THEM AFF.

I'M BLACK AFFRONTED! IMAGINE A' THOSE LADS SEEIN' ME IN MY WELLIES EFTER A'!

By the time Paw's done his stuff—

These are TEA-shirts, right enough!

Oh, my golly!—

See this giant lolly!

Paw thought he knew whit he was daein'—

But now his two pound's down the drain!

AT THE BUT AN' BEN—

THERE! THAT'S IT FINISHED.

BUT WHAT DO YOU WANT A WOODSHED FOR?

STORING WOOD FOR OUR WINTER WEEKENDS WILL SAVE US A FORTUNE!

COME ON, YOU LOT. WE'LL GO INTO THE VILLAGE AND GET SOME FIREWOOD TO PUT IN THE SHED.

AND I KEN WHO'LL HAVE TO CARRY IT BACK.

BUT—

SORRY! WE'VE NO FIREWOOD LEFT.

JUST THEN—

HEY! THERE'S A LAD WI' A LOAD O' STICKS. PERHAPS THEY'RE FOR SALE.

HE'S A SHIFTY-LOOKING CHARACTER. I WOULDNA HAE ANYTHING TO DO WI' HIM, PAW.

ARE YE SELLIN' THOSE STICKS?

AYE! MAKE ME AN OFFER.

THAT'S TYPICAL! PAW NEVER LISTENS TO ME.

AND—

I KNEW WHAT I WAS DOING. ALL THOSE STICKS FOR £2. WHIT A BARGAIN.

BACK AT THE BUT AN' BEN—

HEY! WHERE'S MY SHED GONE?

HO-HO! THAT SCRUFFY LAD SOLD YOU YOUR OWN SHED.

SO YOU KNEW WHIT YOU WERE DOING, DID YOU? YOU DAFT GOWK!

Just for once—

Is Horace a dunce?

Hen doesn't get far—

With his borrowed car!

A tall dark stranger? Whit a laugh!—

But it comes true for Hen, no' half!

Gran'paw Broon is oot o' luck—

He thinks he's smart, but he comes unstuck!

Well, well, well! Did you ever see—

Such a funny-looking family tree?

No " L " plates for Maw Broon now—

She's a driving star, and how!

Tony's sure the best—

He's a CUT above the rest!

Gran'paw's got a date—

But wait . . !

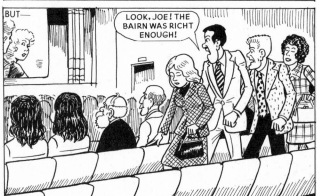

The family's in a proper tizzy—

When Gran'paw Broon keeps feeling dizzy!

Paw can't figure out—

What this is all about!

hese four scroungers think it's awfy—

No' tae get their cup o' coffee!

What a shock when they meet—

Spotty Danny in the street

You've never heard the like—

Maw says she's going on strike

Big Mick Mauler—

Is no' a welcome caller!

Poor Daphne's face falls!

Gran'paw shouldn't eat—

This special kind of sweet!

YE'LL LOSE YOUR TEETH IF YOU EAT TOO MANY SWEETS, BAIRN.

LATER—

HAE A PEPPERMINT! THEY'RE EXTRA-STRONG, BROON.

THANKS! I'LL TAK' A COUPLE. ONE FOR EACH CHEEK.

THEY'RE TOO NIPPY TAE GIVE TAE THE BAIRN.

SUDDENLY—

COUGH! SPLUTTER! WHIT A HEAT!

POOR BROON! I'LL GIVE HIS BACK A SLAP . . .

HELP! MY TEETH HAVE LANDED IN THAT BUSH!

I CANNA SEE THEM.

THEY'RE NO' OVER HERE.

MAW WAS RIGHT! YOU DO LOSE YOUR TEETH IF YE EAT TOO MANY SWEETS.

There are black looks for Paw Broon—

When this visitor sits doon!

If ye want tae run—

Here's how it's done!

One clout at that nail—

Then hear them wail!

Oh, whit a caper—

When Paw wants a paper!

Paw Broon's well equipped today—

But there's one thing he DOESNA hae!

Too many trips to the barber's chair—

Leave poor Hen Broon in despair!

The Bairn knows just who should be—

Tucking in to this daffodil tea!

One good laughter hoot—

And guess what shoots right oot!

Sounds bad, but is it?

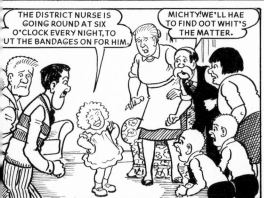

It's a funny scene—

When the Broons look green!

Here's a " diet "—

Tae keep folk quiet!

. . . but they'll no' get a seat—

On Gran'paw's new " suite"

Is Maw poorly? Is Maw ill?

They're all worried stiff—until . . .

Paw thinks he's smart, but there's a catch—

He's " hot stuff " at this cricket match!

ust what has this auld lad planned—

When he lends folk a helping hand?

If your TV's broken doon—

Just ring for Bairn Broon.

Shifting furniture's no joke—

Now Paw's sorry that he spoke!

Auld age has its compensations—

Gran'paw tells a' his relations!

How's this for meals—

On four big wheels?

Close shaves galore—

And there's still one more!

IT'S YOUR ARMY RE-UNION THE NICHT, PAW! YE'D BETTER GET READY!

THERE'S PLENTY O' TIME YET! HERE, DID I EVER TELL YE ABOOT THE CLOSE SHAVE I HAD IN EGYPT?

ABOOT A HUNDRED TIMES!

TEN MINUTES LATER—

...AYE, THAT WAS A NARROW ESCAPE. WE HAD A CLOSE SHAVE IN ITALY TOO. WE'D JUST...

NO' THAT AULD STORY AGAIN!

TEN MORE MINUTES LATER—

...I WAS LUCKY THAT TIME, BUT THE CLOSE SHAVE DURING THE BOMBING RAID WAS EVEN WORSE...

SILLY AULD BLETHER!

SUDDENLY—

...BUT I'M USED TAE CLOSE SHAVES... OH, NO! IS THAT THE TIME? I'LL BE LATE IF I DINNA HURRY!

SO—

MY BUS LEAVES IN FIVE MINUTES BUT I'VE ONLY GOT TAE SHAVE!

JUST THEN—

OH, NO! THE LIGHTS HAVE FUSED!

DINNA WORRY! I'LL FIX THEM IN TEN MINUTES!

BUT I CANNA WAIT THAT LONG AND I CANNA SHAVE IN THE DARK!

THERE ARE LIGHTS IN THE CLOSE. YE COULD SHAVE OOT THERE!

I DINNA HAE ONY CHOICE!

SO—

THIS IS RIDICULOUS. FANCY HAVIN' TAE SHAVE OOT ON THE STAIRS!

BUT YE TOLD US YE WERE USED TAE CLOSE SHAVES, PAW!

What's got into Joe today? —

He winna let the youngsters play!

Gran'paw's acting awfy cocky—

Does he plan to be a jockey?

Maggie's meals make Paw Broon wince—

All he wants is tatties and mince!

If the barometer says " Wet "—

Then that's what they'll get

You'll soon see why—

The Bairn's so " fly "

Paw thinks the rest are silly asses—

But see HIS kind o' fancy glasses!

There's a shock for Maggie when—

She tries to forget the But an' Ben

With boring tails o' line and rod—

The Broons are off to the Land of Nod!

This is the place—

For a funny sack race

he berries Gran'paw picks—

Lead to walking sticks!

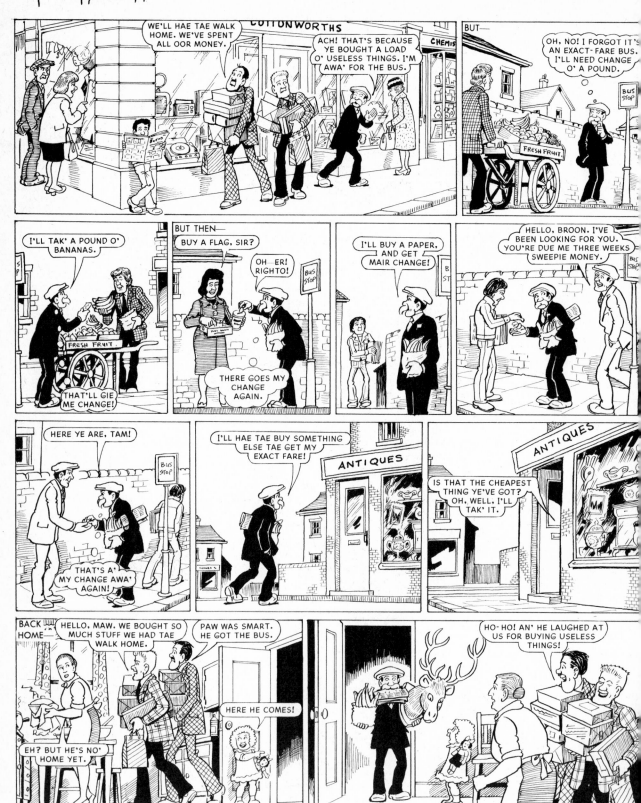

Gran'paw Broon puts Daph in her place—

And then he gets a real red face!

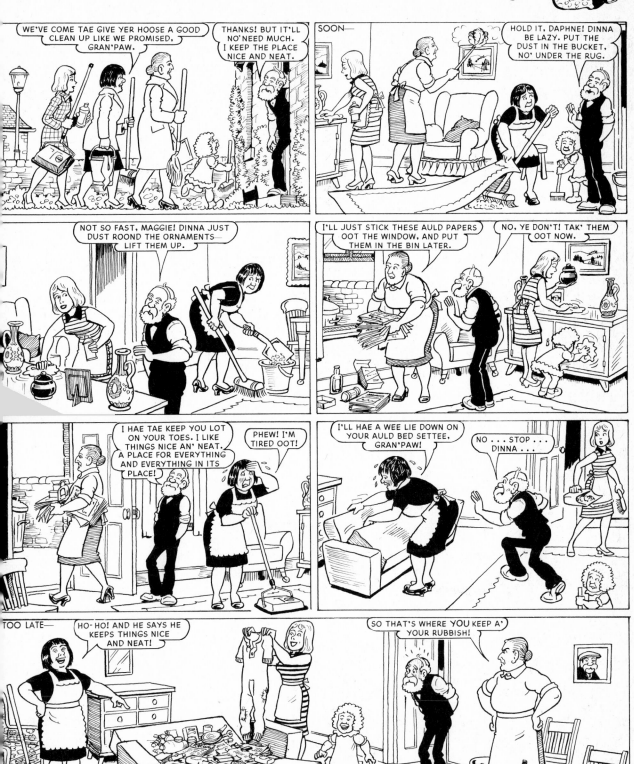

Paw's a winner all the way—

That's why he's filled with dismay!

Here's the tale of a key—

It's a real TEA-hee!

When Hen opens that box!

Poor Paw's in a sorry plight—

It seems he can't tell left from right!

Crafty tricks—

With candlesticks!

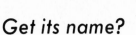

No wonder Paw Broon's in dismay—

'Sno fun when Sammy comes to play

See the family's outsize grins—

When Paw and Gran'paw meet their twins!

What a to-do—

When the clock strikes two

Doesn't bring grins!

There are plastic trees and plastic holly—

And plastic other things, by golly

See the gloomy faces when—

It's Christmas Day at No. 10!